DETECTIVE DAN

Alison Maloney & Antonia Woodward

meadowside
CHILDREN'S BOOKS

Dan's tummy rumbled and grumbled. The smell of Mum's freshly-baked cookies wafted towards him...

But wait, what's this?
All gone?

Who could have taken
his tasty treat?

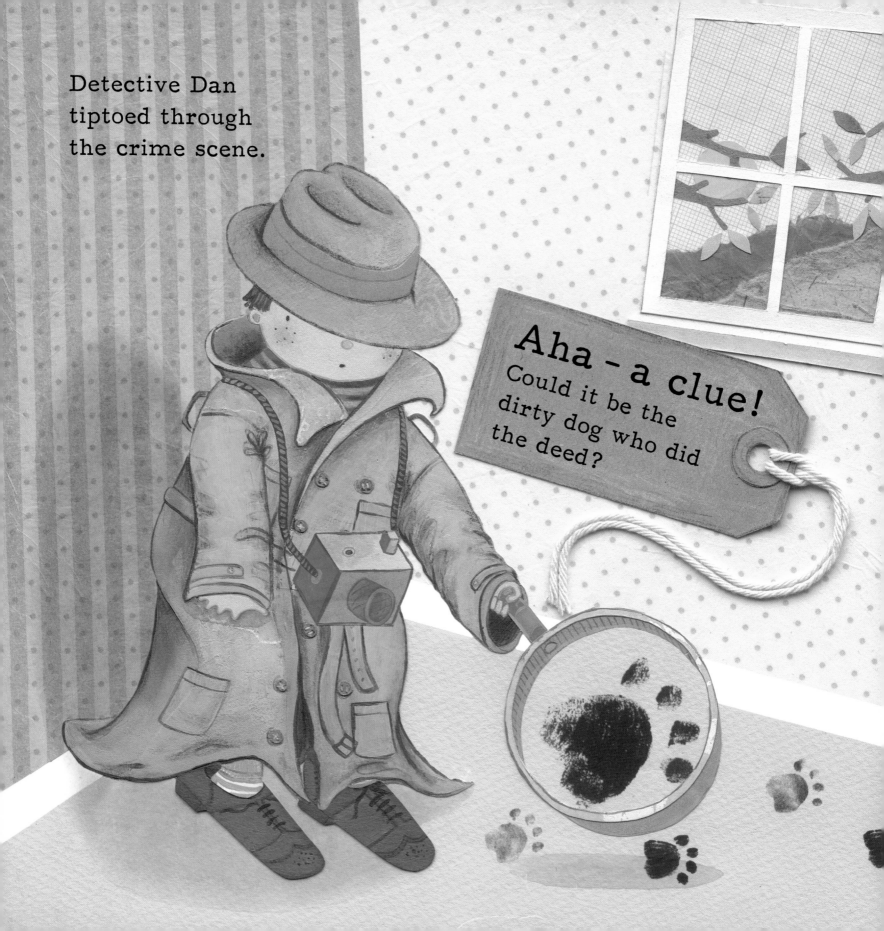

Detective Dan tiptoed through the crime scene.

Aha – a clue! Could it be the dirty dog who did the deed?

CASE FILE
SUSPECT NO. 1

Traces of mud on bone

Dog's bone

Empty basket

Newly-dug hole

Dan followed
the trail until...

he found the playful pup
lazing on the lawn.

Another clue!
Could it be the
crafty cat who
committed the crime?

SUSPECT NO. 2

Empty plate

Milk
(perfect with cookies)

pawprints!

Dan followed the trail until...

he found the clever kitty snoozing in the sun.

Another clue!
Could it be my bothersome brother who bagged the biscuits?

SUSPECT NO. 3

Change of clothes
(to cover tracks?)

Rocket-making kit

Football mags!

Dan followed the trail until...

he found the busy boy
bouncing a ball.

Another clue!
Could it be my
sneaky sister who
snaffled the snack?

SUSPECT
NO. 4

Girl's hat

Doll's stuff

Colouring in

Dan followed
the trail until...

he found the giggling girl
dancing with her dolls.

Time for Detective Dan
to examine the suspects...

clue!

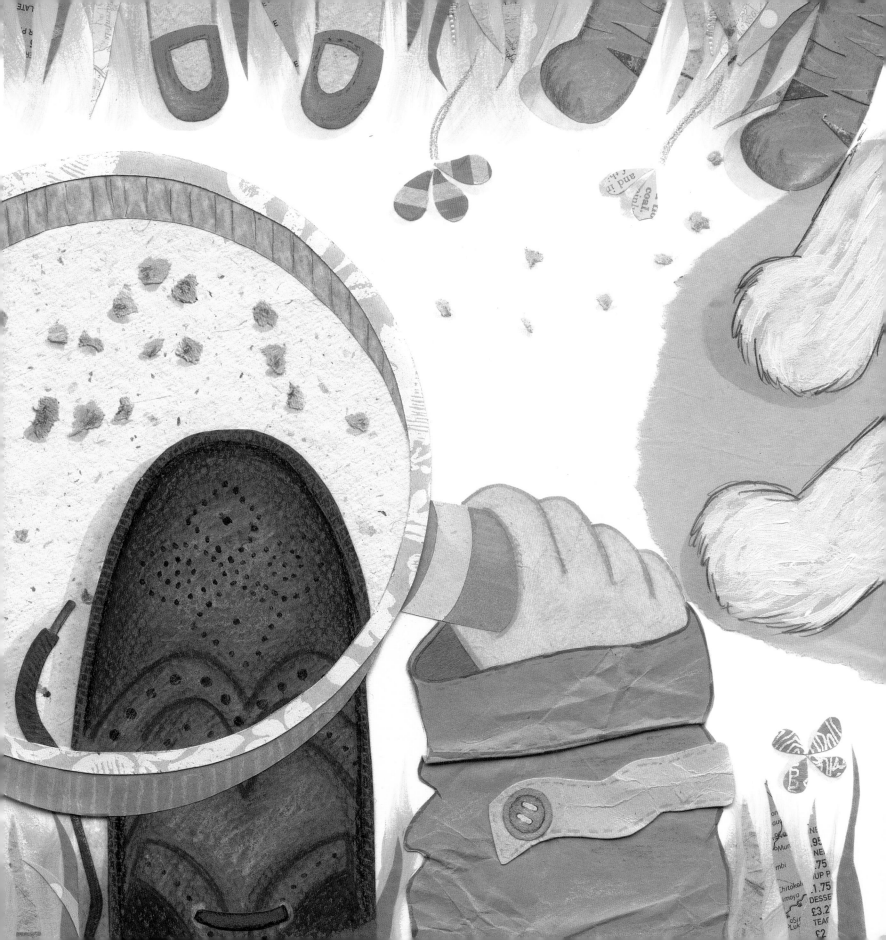

Detective Dan followed the trail one more time...

Start here X

Cat + Jool X

From the kitchen...

Dog X

where
he found...

For Joe, with love
A.M.

For my wonderful family
and my wonderful God,
the Prince of Peace
A.W.

First published in 2012 by Meadowside Children's Books, 185 Fleet Street, London EC4A 2HS
www.meadowsidebooks.com

Text © Alison Maloney 2012 · Illustrations © Antonia Woodward 2012

The rights of Alison Maloney and Antonia Woodward to be identified as the author and illustrator of this work
have been asserted by them in accordance with the Copyright, Designs and Patents Act, 1988

A CIP catalogue record for this book is available from the British Library
1 3 5 7 9 10 8 6 4 2

Paper used in the production of this book is a natural,
recyclable product from wood grown in sustainable forests

Printed in China